Beyond Imagination

Edited By Allie Jones

First published in Great Britain in 2023 by:

Young Writers
Remus House
Coltsfoot Drive
Peterborough
PE2 9BF
Telephone: 01733 890066
Website: www.youngwriters.co.uk

Book Design by Ashley Janson

Softback ISBN 978-1-80459-858-0

Printed and bound in the UK by BookPrintingUK
Website: www.bookprintinguk.com
YB0MA0028B

FOREWORD

Welcome Reader,

For Young Writers' latest competition The Big Green Poetry Machine, we asked primary school pupils to craft a poem about the world. From nature and environmental issues to exploring their own habitats or those of others around the globe, it provided pupils with the opportunity to share their thoughts and feelings about the world around them.

Here at Young Writers our aim is to encourage creativity in children and to inspire a love of the written word, so it's great to get such an amazing response, with some absolutely fantastic poems. It's important for children to be aware of the world around them and some of the issues we face, but also to celebrate what makes it great! This competition allowed them to express their hopes and fears or simply write about their favourite things. The Big Green Poetry Machine gave them the power of words and the result is a wonderful collection of inspirational and moving poems in a variety of poetic styles.

I'd like to congratulate all the young poets in this anthology; I hope this inspires them to continue with their creative writing.

CONTENTS

St Matthew's CE Primary School, West Wimbledon

Kieran Varma (8) 81

St Matthew's Primary School, Belfast

Patrick Turley (10) 82
Aidan Graham (10) 83

St Thomas' Primary School, Riddrie

Rhia McCormack (8) 84
Keren Moore (9) 85
Olly Smith (8) 86
Caris Gemmell (8) 87
Tyrone Kamau (9) 88
Matteo Dei Rossi (8) 89
Joseph McLaughlin (8) 90

Suffah Primary School, Hounslow

Eliza Hunjra (11) 91
Salma Mohamud (11) 92

Woodland Community Primary School, Heywood

Loxy Hall (10) 93
Jayden Baker (10) 94
Tommy Cox (10) 95
Teddy Warwick (9) 96
Jaydan Wright (10) 97
Marko Nigus (7) 98
David Knight (10) 99
Elisia Brooks (7) 100
Ollie Prichard (9) 101
Charlie Hegarty (8) 102
Maryam Ghilas (8) 103
Declan Millward (7) 104
Oliver Tunstall (7) 105
Roman Richards (8) 106

Ysgol Gymraeg Henllan, Henllan

Elizabeth Vaughan-Hepple (9) 107

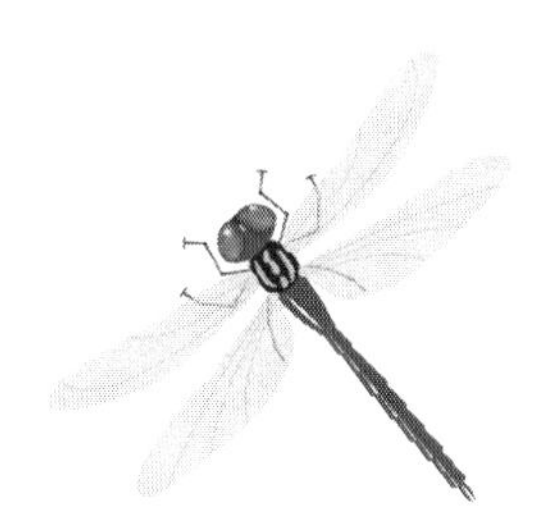

THE POEMS

Polar Bear

A kennings

Arctic king
Stalking beast
Seal eater
Alone hunter
White fighter
Heavy mammal
Russian animal
Evil bear
Furry hair
Cold weather
Fish catcher
Furious eyes
Ice lover
Stealth swimmer.

Yusuf Elsebakhy (9)
Abercrombie Primary School, Chesterfield

Cat

A kennings

Fast species
Fuzzy, cute
Full of energy
Very crazy
Flexible, small
Long body
White whiskers
Tiny ears
Pink nose
Little paws
Soft hair
Sharp claws
Black patterns
White stripes.

Eva Palfreyman (9)
Abercrombie Primary School, Chesterfield

Dad

When I cry, he makes it dry,
He buys me stuff that helps my knowledge,
When I'm sad, he cheers me up by doing funny stuff like doing what monkeys do.
When I fall, he picks me up and makes me happy,
When we go out, he holds my hand and doesn't let go,
When I go on a ride, he will always go on with me,
When I'm hungry and Mum's not home,
He will make me a sandwich or he will just give me a snack,
When I'm tired, he will tuck me in my blanket and lie down with me,
When I'm scared, he will come and tell me, "Don't be scared, there are no monsters, they are not real."

Hamzah Patel (9)
Azhar Academy Primary School, Leytonstone

And That's The Truth

I have been around the world twice,
And that's the truth.
I have been the strongest man in the world,
And that's the truth.
I have met Neil Armstrong.
And that's the truth.
I have a very big lion in my garden,
And that's the truth.
I have my very own big chunk of gold and silver,
And that's the truth.
I have been to Antarctica and the Arctic,
And that's the truth.
I have my very own mansion and a Rolls Royce,
And that's the truth.
I have my own sports car,
And that's the truth.
All right, all right, all right,
I have everything,
And that's the truth.
All right, all right, all right,

I am the biggest liar in the whole entire universe,
And that's the truth.

Hammaad Hajee (8)
Azhar Academy Primary School, Leytonstone

Fat Cat

My fat cat sits all day and night,
Eating cookies all the time,
I tell him to stop sitting every day,
But the sofa is his place to stay!

My fat cat once saw a dog,
The first time I saw him run,
Pow! Smash! He punched his enemy,
The dog had a bruise on his nose,
Surprisingly, my cat smashed his bones!
The dog never saw the cat or me,
He never messed with the cat ever again.

Would you like a cat like this?
I sure wouldn't because he only sits on the couch,
And all he does all day is slouch.

Abiha Rana (9)
Azhar Academy Primary School, Leytonstone

And That's The Truth

I'm way stronger than my dad,
And that's the truth.
I'm 800 years old,
And that's the truth.
I have £5 million pounds,
And that's the truth.
I have a pet bull,
And that's the truth.
I also have a lion in my room,
And that's the truth.
I know my 800 times table,
And that's the truth.
I have five phones,
And that's the truth.
I have five laptops,
And that's the truth.
I made it all up,
And that's the truth!

Ibraheem Qaisar (7)
Azhar Academy Primary School, Leytonstone

My Fat Cat

My fat cat lays on her red mat,
All day and all night,
She never gets off the couch,
All she does all day is slouch,
I hope she stops now!

My fat cat wears a blue hat,
She likes it when I pat her head with a bat,
Her fur is silky and grey,
And she was born in the month of May.

Even though she once killed a rat,
I still love my fat, grey cat!

Sameya Kiani (9)
Azhar Academy Primary School, Leytonstone

Smart

S mart is something that it's really good to be
M aths makes you the smartest and makes you smart
A nd being smart makes your brain so much better
R eally good and fantastic it would be to be the smartest on Earth
T he Earth is really big, gigantic and enormous, so it would be difficult to be the smartest on the whole entire Earth.

Rayeed Iftekhar (8)
Azhar Academy Primary School, Leytonstone

My Family

My family are the best,
And they always try their best.
My family are the best,
They can't get a rest.
My family are the best,
They can't get in a mess.

Khadijah Abdula-Latif (7)
Azhar Academy Primary School, Leytonstone

Save The Environment

E ntertaining to plant trees
N o more meat, just eat some greens
V ital to plant some trees
I advise you to eat beans
R eally sad to see the plants died
O n the day, they will cry
N o more electronics, go outside
M any people don't know
E ven that it's eco day
N oble is what you'll be when we see you plant trees
T oday is planting day, grab a bunch of seeds

D o your best to help the rest
A pples are planted
Y ou are noble is what you'll get.

Isabella Amoako-Prempeh (11)
Bandon Hill Primary School, Wallington

Save The Environment, Now!

Stop littering because
Did you know
When you litter
You are polluting as well?
Because you are harming animals all around the world
Even in the sea
Because people throw rubbish into the sea.
Did you know
When you start your car engine
That is pollution?
Because it's basically gas
And gas has a lot of chemicals in it
That can harm a lot of animals.
Did you know
Underneath your car
There's like a smell?
And some have fish smells on them that attract foxes and cats
And other things that like fish

And other kinds of food
Everyone is responsible for the environment
Actually for the whole world.

Jaiden Ramsurrun (8)
Bandon Hill Primary School, Wallington

Rainforest

R ainforest is in danger.
A nimals are dying.
I want to help.
N ever chop the trees down.
F ire hurts the animals.
O h! The rainforest is in danger.
R ecycle your trash.
E veryone can make a difference.
S top wasting paper.
T ogether we can make a change.

Hamza Sidar (9)
Bandon Hill Primary School, Wallington

Elephant

E very elephant is in danger
L ovely, big, beautiful creatures.
E lephants are going extinct.
P lease stop locking them in little cages.
H elp the animals.
A nimals need you.
N ow is your time to help elephants!
T ogether we can do this.

Ronnie Leigh Heard (9)
Bandon Hill Primary School, Wallington

Our Planet

I am a long-necked animal
We are yellow with a brown pattern
We are herbivores
We are land animals
We regurgitate our food
We drink water
We mostly eat leaves
What am I?

Answer: I am a giraffe.

Rhys Phillips (9)
Bandon Hill Primary School, Wallington

Earth

E nergy
A lways recycling
R euse
T urn off lights
H elp our planet.

Tallulah Mulcahy-Cox (10)
Bandon Hill Primary School, Wallington

Nature's Trees

Tall as the sky and rough like a rock
How can no one be impressed by me?
Growing my branches as quickly as a clock
I'm relaxing, calm and soothing to see

Look at me and wait outside my door
Standing strong with my leaf and friends
I recall that paper matters more
Cutting trees down it never ends

The wonder of my own great, green mother
Stop chopping trees down one after another

No more! No more! No more!

I will be really pleased
If you can save the trees.

Maya Hussain (10)
Bankfoot Primary School, Bradford

Save Our Trees

S ave our trees
A nimals need trees
V aluable
E nvironment needs trees

O pen your heart to the environment
U nreal animals are in danger
R ainforests are part of the environment

T rees are beautiful and need to be saved
R ain helps the environment
E arth is being ruined
E njoy the Earth
S ave the trees because trees are being cut down.

Archie Povey (10)
Beck Row Primary Academy, Beck Row

Animals

E nergy in people
N ature is nice
V ery many animals
I n nature, there are leaves
R eally good people
O n the trees
N ext to a river
M ean birds
E njoyed the time
N o littering
T rying to clean.

Archie Southey (11)
Beck Row Primary Academy, Beck Row

Turtles

T urtles are losing numbers
U nless we can do something
R eal change is needed
T ogether, we can work together
L ooking after turtles
E veryone, start saving the turtles
S ave the world.

Loretta Watts (7)
Beck Row Primary Academy, Beck Row

Protect The Earth

P rotect our world
R ecycle our rubbish
O ur world should be tidy
T rees need help
E veryone clean the Earth
C an you always save the ocean?
T he animals need our help.

Cody-James Garbould (7)
Beck Row Primary Academy, Beck Row

Nature

N o to litter
A nd put rubbish in the bin
T he environment is bad
U are putting the world in danger
R ubbish, please clean it up
E nvironment is in danger.

Reggie Bartlett (10)
Beck Row Primary Academy, Beck Row

Come To Beck Row Beacon

B eautiful display, it happens
E ach year, everyone's welcome
A mazing atmosphere
C ome to Beck Row
O pen to everyone
N ature reserve.

Riley Blowers (11)
Beck Row Primary Academy, Beck Row

Save The Earth

E veryone, clean the world
A lways help humans when they get hurt
R emember to save the world
T he animals need our help
H elp the planet.

Ronnie Bartlett (7)
Beck Row Primary Academy, Beck Row

Help To Save The Flowers

E veryone, be happy!
A lways save animals
R emember to be helpful
T he Earth is hurt
H elp the flowers.

Layla Goldthorpe (6)
Beck Row Primary Academy, Beck Row

Nature

A kennings poem

Rainforest saver,
Earth helper,
Plastic recycler,
Leaf jumper,
Animal rider,
Leaf maker.

Owen Horan (5)
Beck Row Primary Academy, Beck Row

What Am I?

People dump 5.25 trillion trash on me every year
I keep some animals alive
I provide food for humans
I provide oxygen
I protect the climate
What am I?

Answer: The ocean.

Caius Garcia (9)
Bickley Park School, Bickley

A Poem About Nature

Nature is beautiful,
Butterflies are flitting.
Time is flying,
Animals are dying.
Save the Earth,
Help animals give birth.
Save the animals,
Save the Earth.

Nature is everything to us,
Trees, flowers and desert plants.
Grow trees for oxygen,
Clean the environment.
Save our lively Planet Earth.

Aaranya Sivananth (7)
Blair Peach Primary School, Southall

Deforestation Affects Our Planet

R aise awareness of the problem
A tmosphere damaged by greenhouse gases
I n our hands, lay the problem
N o trees, no humans
F ewer crops
O xygen is good for us
R isk of drought and disease
E arth needs our help
S ave our wildlife from their habitat destruction
T rees are good for the planet.

Lewis Atkin (9)
Chilham St Mary's CE Primary School, Chilham

Deforestation

A haiku

Deforestation
Stop cutting down the trees now
Save our planet Earth!

Adam Guelleh (10)
Chilham St Mary's CE Primary School, Chilham

I Love Nature

I love nature, I love rain
I love the dreams inside my brain
I love the wind when I open the door
I love when I hit the floor
When the trees sway around
I spot a bit of plastic on the ground
I go and pick it up and bin it
Then I walk to school to learn some more
After school I go home
To play and play and take a rest
Then I go outside to protect our world
Because I love nature
I love nature, I love family, I love friends.

Emma Sims (7)
Dursley CofE Primary School, Dursley

Frogs

Frogs are poisonous, frogs eat flies
I love frogs because they jump so high

There are 7,3000 species of frogs
Over 265 million years old
Some people think their blood is hot
When we know it is cold

Its house is a habitat
They have webbed feet
I love frogs because they're pretty neat.

Nova Trinder (7)
Dursley CofE Primary School, Dursley

A Field Of Poppies And Roses

The field has poppies that are so pretty
They catch your eye instantly
The roses glimmer in the sunlight
They are curly sources of nature
They make us happy
The field with wheat where the poppies grow
In the hedges the wild roses show.

Emilia Turner (9)
Dursley CofE Primary School, Dursley

The Flowers Are So Beautiful

The flowers were so beautiful
The daffodils glowed
The sun shone bright
The leaves drop
The stones shine
The light blue sky with the fluffy clouds
A gigantic smile came to me
As the sun set down
I went home.

Matilda Brimacombe (7)
Dursley CofE Primary School, Dursley

Amazing Arctic

Melting ice,
Takes a price,
Take my advice,
I'll be concise.

Over the years,
Destroyed without care,
By fuel-hungry millionaires.

The floppy seals,
Need a meal,
But you make them feel,
Like a piece of steel.

The ice is melting,
You should be helping,
We need to get protecting.

Jessie Torrance (9)
Ennerdale CE Primary School, Ennerdale Bridge

Don't Litter!

Don't litter because that doesn't help
The environment, turtles, fishes
And underwater creatures.
And we don't like that.
We want to save them.
Not kill them.
So please don't litter.

Bella Clarke (8)
Gosberton Academy, Gosberton

Planet Poem

O cean
U niverse
R ain

P lanet
L iving
A nimal
N ature
E nvironment
T ree.

Eddie Scase (7)
Gosberton Academy, Gosberton

Killing Climate Change!

C ountless animals' lives lost.
L ions killed for the well-wanted riches.
I ce caps melting faster than ever before.
M any people throwing away debris, boosting climate change.
A frica, an already hot country, is becoming unbearable due to climate change.
T usks of elephants being hunted to seek more money for their greedy pockets.
E xtreme weather all around us getting a helping hand due to climate change.

C atastrophic wildfires killing cute koalas and other innocent animals.
H urricanes and tornadoes all around us destroying cities and villages.
A bnormal weather conditions destroying our planet slowly.
N ow we need to take responsibility for out past actions.
G o outside and admire the planet we could lose.
E conomy rising due to the lack of supplies because of climate change. We need to stop climate change!

Harris Cunningham Mason (10)
Hamilton College, Hamilton

Save Our Earth

S coop up all of the plastic in our ocean
A n ocean without suffering
V arious species of fish going extinct
E very little helps

O xygen is vital for a healthy planet
U seless plastics we must stop
R educe, reuse, recycle

E lectric cars can take you far
A nimals can live healthier without plastics
R aging fires are destroying our forests
T he ice caps are melting from the effects of pollution
H elp save our Earth.

Carter Milne (10)
Hamilton College, Hamilton

Nature

Nature can make you mature
But only if you're willing to be.
We could all be living in harmony
If only we kept nature clean.
I'm not saying it is your fault or mine
But it is our community.
And don't lie, you do it too sometimes.
I wish I could say this is a lie
But it is the truth.
So you really cannot deny.

Gursimran Kaur (11)
Henry Green Primary School, Dagenham

Natural Harmony

N ever-ending harmony
A nts and bees with hopping bunnies
T rees covered in luscious green
U nique blossoms, flowers and daisies
R eveal the beauty underneath
E vergreens coloured green.

Areeba Irfan (10)
Henry Green Primary School, Dagenham

Monkey

M onkeys are loving things
O verall, the best animal
N ever-ending best animal
K eep safe
E very animal is cool
Y ou're amazing.

Archie Meade (11)
Henry Green Primary School, Dagenham

The World Of Bugs

Bugs, bugs are amazing creatures.
The caterpillar has lots of features.
Worms wiggle in the dirt.
Beetles' outer shells make sure that they don't get hurt.
Bees and wasps buzz around.
While slugs stay on the ground.
Dragonflies are as fast as lightning.
Spiders are said to be rather frightening.

Bugs, bugs are amazing creatures.
Yes, they are amazing.
But because of the pollution,
They won't be so breathtaking.
Because we're taking their homes.

Archie (10)
Langlands Primary School, Forfar

Ants And Nature

Ants are marvellous things
Some people can't rant about ants
Without nature, ants would die and so would we
Ants are marvellous creatures
We can't stop the ants!

George Philip (10)
Langlands Primary School, Forfar

Environment Is Important

E veryone needs food
N eeds rules
V ery tall trees
I mportant to follow rules
R ules are important to follow
O ther rules
N ice rules
M otorbikes are damaging the environment
E nvironment has rules
N ever litter
T ry to be nice.

Mason Dally (6)
Lunt's Heath Primary School, Widnes

What Am I?

I fly in the sky.
I eat seeds and worms.
I do not live in a cave.
I build a nest in a tree.
I do not like going in the water.
I can see very well.
I live on Earth.
I can almost fly higher than the clouds.
I can see you when you're playing outside.
I can't stay very still.
What am I?

Faith Olivia Winham (7)
Lunt's Heath Primary School, Widnes

The Arctic Adventure

A rctic snow owls
R acing penguins down the mountain
C racking ice
T here are lots of animals that cannot be found anywhere else
I celandic oceans
C reatures around the corner.

Matthew Ellis (6)
Lunt's Heath Primary School, Widnes

What Am I?

I have lots of animals.
I'm very green.
I have trees.
People can visit.
There are flowers.
I'm not in England.
It can be hot.
There are lots of plants.
No wolves but there are cheetahs.

Reuben Humphries (7)
Lunt's Heath Primary School, Widnes

Earth

E arth is
A round us
R ound is an invisible line that goes round
T wo days or three days, I just don't know
H ow does it work, I really want to know.

Isla Doyle (6)
Lunt's Heath Primary School, Widnes

Don't Cut Down The Trees

T rees give us oxygen
R espect the world
E venings, the owls wake
E ggs are in the trees
S top chopping trees down.

Pippa Autumn Jones (7)
Lunt's Heath Primary School, Widnes

What Am I?

I can fly.
I can catch worms and bread.
Sometimes I have baths in gardens.
What am I?

Answer: A bird.

Emilia Davies
Lunt's Heath Primary School, Widnes

My Lovely Village

I hear the sound of katydids, crickets, and cicadas in the night while I am sleeping.
I wake to the sound of the birds twittering.
I wash my face in the cold pond where the goldfish are playing.
I see the bees working.
I feel beautiful the grass beneath my feet as I am walking.
I see the colourful butterflies playing.
I see the spotty cows grazing

This is my beautiful village...

Syeda Khanom (8)
Oasis Academy Hobmoor, Yardley

Neat Nature...

I go outside
I see the sky
If I said it was ugly
That would be a big lie

I look at the glistening lake
Nearby
And the smell of the flowers
Made me feel awake

I saw the trees
Full of emerald leaves
I saw some bright honey
With some lovely bees

I look at myself
I'm grateful for this place
I see a cute deer
And I pick up my pace

I didn't want to scare it
But I couldn't bear it

I wanted its trust
But it put down a fuss

But in the end
Everything's great!

Aroush Kashif (10)

Oasis Academy Hobmoor, Yardley

I Met A Jolly Germ

I met a jolly germ
In the jolly sun
Having the time of his life
Trying to turn

Later that day
A boy came
He was hungry
And he tried to tame

During that day
As he played
He realised
He had the jolly plague

Travel back and forth
He fled
Went to Hobmoor
But oh no!
The plague had spread

The moral of this story is
Don't trash the planet or you will get ill
Because you are breathing in fumes.

Dua Malik (9)
Oasis Academy Hobmoor, Yardley

Pollution

Observe the traffic and pollution
Where is its solution?
I see my own neighbourhood
This sight, it's not a matter to be taken light
I see the leaves and trees crying
And the burnt fallen leaves lying
I wish that it stops soon
Otherwise, we'll have to take refuge on the moon
Plant trees and take care of them
So our lives don't go in vain.

Amara-May Iqbal (11)
Oasis Academy Hobmoor, Yardley

The Recycling Man

He can get everything
And it won't go on the ground
And he saves the Earth from the rubbish
And they will listen to him
He makes people recycle
And they will do their hardest
To make everyone recycle
And they will save the Earth from all the rubbish
Someone can be nice.

Simão Lira (8)
Our Lady's Catholic Primary School, Cowley

To Save The Animals

S ave every animal on Earth
A lot of animals need help
V ery poor people need money
E veryone should be treated equally.

Racheal Adeoye (8)
Our Lady's Catholic Primary School, Cowley

Global Warming

The planet is getting very hot
And something terrible is happening.
Icebergs all around are melting a lot.
We must start changing,
Now!

It's not fair,
That nature suffers,
When we do it in pairs,
The planet becomes better.

Hey, you, look at the bears,
Their home is breaking away
And now it's happening to the hares!
We must do something about climate change,
Delay it,
Permanently!

Chizimife Ekwe (10)
St Aidan's Catholic Primary Academy, Ilford

Saving The Creation

The world has many living
Things to take care of
Animals that are in danger
Of extinction.

However, there is still a
Chance of changing
Ourselves to be better
People.

Instead of destroying
We can save Earth
From burning by the
Sun

Grow more trees, destroy
Factories and make
Something for
Earth.

If we don't stop
All is going to end

And we are all
Going to die.

But, if we take
Things and seriously
Plant trees, we can
Make a change.

Mateo Javier (11)

St George's Cathedral Catholic Primary School, Southwark

Dreams

Dreams can make you feel
Good or bad but most
Of the time they are lovely
And precious.

Dreams of our planets and
A sapphire ocean with
Dolphins we don't want volcanoes
Burning as lava.

Dreams of the universe with
Stars and colours
Sky as clear as glass that
We can dream with
Many things for our beautiful
World.

Sinai Armas Cornejo (11)
St George's Cathedral Catholic Primary School, Southwark

Through The Clouds And Up To God

Earth is as round
As a ball.

Recycle more, clean
Up things that are on
The floor.

Nature always stays
Alive. Never kill animals
That have died.

Through the clouds and
Up to God. The air that
We breathe from. Don't destroy
Our plants and trees.

Nevaeh McPherson (10)
St George's Cathedral Catholic Primary School, Southwark

We Can Stop Climate Change

Climate change, it's a bit strange
How it's affecting other countries' weather
Well... we can make this better
First of all, stop littering the ocean
Is it some type of potion
That you think you can litter in?
If we take care of Earth
We might all rebirth
And a new life and new world
Where it's all safe
And where we're not afraid
About climate change.

Abimbola Tayo (11)
St Joseph's RC Primary School, Bermondsey

Act Now

O ur planet is being torn to shreds
U nhappy animals' death surrounds
R educe, reuse and recycle, to save heads

P rotect the planet, get rid of plastic
L ive life like you're coral in the ocean
A nd stop feeding creatures horrid potions
N ature crying and animals are dying
E xtinct, gone, nothing here is fantastic
T onnes of bottles and bags, life drowns in plastic.

Maya Belaidi (10)
St Joseph's RC Primary School, Bermondsey

Pollution

Pollution has impacted massively
And we really need to find a solution before it's too late
There are many different types of pollution
Air pollution, water pollution, soil pollution
Radioactive pollution and noise pollution
Each has a devastating effect on our planet
And leave us in a habit which keeps our planet unsustainable
I don't have enough time, so I gotta say bye.

Nnamdi Oluh (11)
St Joseph's RC Primary School, Bermondsey

Save Our World

Stop climate change
Stop, stop, stop
Stop deforestation
Save our trees, save our animals' habitats
Reuse paper, reuse plastic
Save our ocean, save our turtles
Stop using fossil fuels
Let's start making a change in Mother Earth!

Ruthmary Andino (10)
St Joseph's RC Primary School, Bermondsey

The Weather Today

Wind, wind, blowing so hard
Wind, wind from afar
Cold, cold like ice-cold
Cold making me shiver like mice
Rain, rain, showering my body
Rain pouring away.

Chibuikem Nnachor (11)
St Joseph's RC Primary School, Bermondsey

Life Equals Earth

How much do you value your life?
What would you say you are worth?
How much would you be prepared to pay
For that life but without the Earth?

Adam Haigh (10)
St Joseph's RC Primary School, Bermondsey

The Earth

In a special place,
Near the mountains not close to school,
There was a special tree
With autumn leaves,
Blowing in the air.
With blossom in my hair
How the mountain wobbled
With lots of leaves on it.

Aliza Border Pearce (8)
St Joseph's RC Primary School, London

Our Planet

O ur planet
U nique in all ways
R educe, reuse, recycle

P ollution needs to stop
L itter is not good for the environment
A ctivity planner
N ever give up on our planet
E nvironment is an important part in our lives
T hankful for everything we have on our planet.

Aizah Fareed (9)
St Margaret's CE Primary School, Great Barr

What Am I?

Strong claws
Six legs
Small teeth
Big eyes
Sea dweller
Hard shell
I can be red, blue or black
I can live in a shell or under a rock
What am I?

Answer: A crab.

Leo Hill (9)
St Margaret's CE Primary School, Great Barr

Save Our Earth

Of all the planets, I am special: I am Mother Earth!
Filled with water, air and life.
Humans, trees, birds, sea animals and wildlife.
I spin and turn all year round the orbit.
To give you all the seasons.

You people use my land, air, water and soil.
But keep on filling it with litter and allowing it to spoil.
I provide you with air, food and a home to live.
With greedy lust, you destroy the nature I give.
The air you fill with smoke
Makes my breath choke.
What was once a clean sea and pure soil
Is now all dull: clogged with waste and oil.

Georgi Mitov (11)
St Mary's Catholic Primary School, Fleetwood

The Planet Earth

We're killing our Earth,
And that's really bad,
Nobody believes us,
Because we are young,
Our forests are turning to ash,
In a second,
Ask Turkey,
They'll tell you about it,
They'll tell you how,
They have lost their homes,
While we keep a blind eye,
And chat on our phones,
For the last time,
This is not a joke,
Our factories are working,
And toxins admitting,
The ozone is crumbling,
And we won't stop putting,
Chemicals in what we're trying to breathe,
Our future is stolen,
And we are the thieves,

The coral reefs are dying,
And no one is helping,
Do you realise those keep oceans alive?
This started back in 1985!
This Earth fills us with,
Hope and lush,
It gives us the most worth,
As much as we love our tide,
We don't help together worldwide,
Our weather begins to provide,
Litter fills our air with bitter,
Most of the percent of us,
Leave the Earth to rot,
While others begin to patch,
These bullet shots,
Our eco is dropping,
Our ego begins to fade,
This isn't the world,
That we made,
We raise this place,
Piece by piece,
This world only praises us,

It fixes our problems like creases,
We can forgive ourselves,
Day by day,
And that's what we pray.

Akeefah Meah (10)

St Mary's Catholic Primary School, Fleetwood

Leave The Trees Alone

The grass is green,
The sun is bright,
But the trees are in pain,
Every night.

There's an axe,
In the forest,
And Boris Johnson,
Didn't even try to stop it.

Kids are playing,
Having fun,
While adults are making money
Just tons.

Don't chop down trees,
It won't help,
We don't want our oxygen
To be locked away.

Hear the trees,
They're on their knees,
Begging for help.

Millie Jones (9)
St Mary's Catholic Primary School, Fleetwood

Green Green Grass

Every flower in the garden is making different faces at me.
Some look happy when I pass by.
And others droop but they are shy.
Some have their heads thrown back to sing.
As I go by.
As I go by, they sing to me.
While I look back.

Lillie Steel (11)
St Mary's Catholic Primary School, Fleetwood

Animals

A nimals are in danger and I don't like that
N o animals should be in danger
I really don't like animals in danger, they are screaming
M ost of the animals are already hurt
A ll different species should be with family like us
L uckily for some animals, they are safe
S o please help the animals, then I will be happy, thank you.

Kieran Varma (8)
St Matthew's CE Primary School, West Wimbledon

Our Planet

S ave the world
A nimals are dying
V ery little population in the world
E normous elephants

O ur planet is losing hope
U nder pressure, our world needs help
R eplanting trees for more oxygen

P lease help the animals
L et the trees stay
A nd also
N ow millions die every year
E verybody needs to love the planet
T ell people: "The animals are okay."

Patrick Turley (10)
St Matthew's Primary School, Belfast

Nature

N ature is all around us
A nice nature walk
T reat nature well, the way you treat yourself
U p in the sky, birds fly high
R ecycle and protect nature from harm
E verywhere there is nature.

Aidan Graham (10)
St Matthew's Primary School, Belfast

Polar Bears

P olar bears only have babies November to January
O nto hunting they go for their cubs
L ooking for males to mate
A rctic is their home
R est is not there for adult polar bears

B abies will play with brothers and sisters
E ast is always North
A cub will stay with their mom for two years
R est is important for cubs
S ometimes the adults will rest.

Rhia McCormack (8)
St Thomas' Primary School, Riddrie

Polar Bears

P olar bears live in the Arctic.
O n the ice they get stuck.
L ooking for food every day.
A ll the polar bears are getting stuck.
R eally hard to live with climate change.

B e kinder to our polar bears.
E ating not enough food.
A ll the animals are suffering.
R escue them from global warming.
S ave the animals.

Keren Moore (9)
St Thomas' Primary School, Riddrie

Polar Bears

P olar bears' skin isn't white, it's transparent.
O nly in cold wilds, polar bears are found in Russia.
L ots of them are predators.
A rctic is so cold.
R eally hard to survive.

B ears weigh up to 700kg.
E very bit of ice is melting.
A nimals are suffering.
R eally big animals.
S ave the animals.

Olly Smith (8)
St Thomas' Primary School, Riddrie

Polar Bears

P olar bears live in the Arctic.
O n the ice, the polar bears slide.
L ooking for food.
A ll of the food is helpful.
R eally cold in the Arctic.

B e careful on the ice.
E arth is warming up.
A ll the animals are suffering.
R un away from the predators.
S ome of the ice is melting.

Caris Gemmell (8)
St Thomas' Primary School, Riddrie

Polar Bears

P olar bears love the Arctic
O n the ice for humans, it is hard to stick on ice
L ooking for food to eat
A ll the ice is melting
R eally hard to swim.

B e kinder to our planet
E arth is warming up
A nimals are suffering
R escue them from global warming
S ave the polar bears!

Tyrone Kamau (9)
St Thomas' Primary School, Riddrie

Penguins

P enguins live in the Antarctic
E arth is warming up, it is bad for penguins
N early too warm, they might get extinct
G lobal warming is bad for penguins
U ntil we stop littering, it will get worse
I n Antarctica, there are Arctic foxes too
N early all the ice is gone
S ave penguins!

Matteo Dei Rossi (8)
St Thomas' Primary School, Riddrie

Arctic

A rctic is like a blanket of snow
R eally cold, even below freezing temperatures
C an I live there?
T hat's something I'll never know
I n the summer, it's still cold
C an you live there?

Joseph McLaughlin (8)
St Thomas' Primary School, Riddrie

Don't Wait!

The forest trees sway at night
The breeze flows without a fright
I hear the trembling trees' plight
Whilst humans wipe them out using all their might

Is it time to be helpful?
Are we ready to be grateful?
How can we become so forgetful?
Every effort can be influential

Come out of your houses
Leave the money pouches
The forests are waiting for a saviour
It is time to change our behaviour

Mother Nature is loving
Let its beauty live
If you ignore its plea
It will never forget nor forgive.

Eliza Hunjra (11)
Suffah Primary School, Hounslow

Environment

Pollution is going on in every country and town,
We need to stop polluting
Because we're ruining our beloved planet Earth.
If we work as a team
You will see that the Earth will be clean,
Now or never,
Let's save the world forever.

Salma Mohamud (11)
Suffah Primary School, Hounslow

I Remember When...

I remember when...
The animals didn't have to worry about the meaning of sadness...
But now they don't need to be taught because they now know themselves...

I remember when...
The ocean made the world as bright as the sun does...
But now the ocean makes the Earth as dark as the moon does

I remember when...
We all knew the ocean was safe and sound...
But now the devil in disguise stepped in the water it has all changed around...

I remember when...
The ocean was like a perfect fantasy...
Now it's a tsunami of devils...

Loxy Hall (10)
Woodland Community Primary School, Heywood

Save The World

Keep the bees in the trees or they might sting your knees.
You might feel sore when the water covers the floor.
Wait until the Earth starts to fall before your eyes and animals start to die.
All the animals you adore you won't be able to see anymore.
Walk instead of drive if you want to keep animals alive.
Think about when you're smiling and others are crying.
Animals are crying and dying and tomorrow you will feel sorrow.
Stop wasting you're time committing crimes
Instead don't litter because the world might get bitter.

Jayden Baker (10)
Woodland Community Primary School, Heywood

Helping Earth

H ow can we stop this madness?
E arth is dying.
L itter is the whole problem.
P ollution is spreading everywhere.
I n need, we need to help.
N o more litter.
G rass is dying by the second.

E xtinction is on the way.
A t the moment, it's not looking good.
R ecycle to save poor animals' lives.
T ogether we shall help the environment.
H elp the animals.

Tommy Cox (10)
Woodland Community Primary School, Heywood

I Remember When...

I remember when...
The calm sandy beaches were filled with glistening sand
I remember when...
The kids ran across the sandy beach with joy on their faces
Meet-ups now are the only things with rubbish
I remember when...
Dolphins, turtles and fish swam here
Now only rubbish swims here
I remember when...
I never had a worry in the world.

Teddy Warwick (9)
Woodland Community Primary School, Heywood

Save Our World

Our planet is being destroyed
Our Earth is crying because we are destroying,
Animals are crying and dying
The ice caps are crying.

Twinkle, twinkle little star
How I wonder what you are
Up above the world so bright
Looking down on the Earth to night.

Stop
Stop using lots of electricity...
Sea levels are rising.

Jaydan Wright (10)
Woodland Community Primary School, Heywood

The Earth

Our incredible, amazing Earth is being destroyed
The blue, glistening sea
The tall green trees
The beautiful clean Earth
Now the polluted ugly Earth
We need kind, helpful humans
Cute, adorable animals.

Marko Nigus (7)
Woodland Community Primary School, Heywood

Gorillas

G orillas need saving
O ur animals need help
R ipping the jungle
I am sad
L eave the Earth
L eave the Earth
A nimals in danger
S ave our Earth.

David Knight (10)
Woodland Community Primary School, Heywood

Tiger

T eeth so sharp
I ntelligent big cats
G reat big claws
E ars are big
R eally lazy.

Elisia Brooks (7)
Woodland Community Primary School, Heywood

All About Oceans

Sharks can be dangerous.
Fish are friendly.
Plastic bottles are ugly.
Plastic is killing our ocean animals.

Ollie Prichard (9)
Woodland Community Primary School, Heywood

Leopard

A haiku

High leaping leopard
Leaping as high as a broom
Loving, loud leopard.

Charlie Hegarty (8)
Woodland Community Primary School, Heywood

Panda

A haiku

Panda loves bamboo
Climbing the trees carefully
It is time for lunch.

Maryam Ghilas (8)
Woodland Community Primary School, Heywood

Rhino

A haiku

Rhino running fast
Running at its fastest speed
Hoping it survives.

Declan Millward (7)
Woodland Community Primary School, Heywood

Pandas

A haiku

Panda munching grass
Sitting on the muddy ground
It is endangered.

Oliver Tunstall (7)
Woodland Community Primary School, Heywood

Rhino

A haiku

Rhino runs quickly
Rhino runs outrageously
They are endangered.

Roman Richards (8)
Woodland Community Primary School, Heywood

Climate Change

C hange the planet we need to do
L and is burning
I ce is melting
M ake the world better
A nimals need help
T ake care of the world
E arth needs more trees

C limate change is bad
H ealth the animals need to be fed well
A ll over the world is good and bad
N ever cut trees
G ive the animals enough food
E very time you finish a bottle of water you must
put it in the bin.

Elizabeth Vaughan-Hepple (9)
Ysgol Gymraeg Henllan, Henllan

YOUNG WRITERS INFORMATION

We hope you have enjoyed reading this book – and that you will continue to in the coming years.

If you're the parent or family member of an enthusiastic poet or story writer, do visit our website **www.youngwriters.co.uk/subscribe** and sign up to receive news, competitions, writing challenges and tips, activities and much, much more! There's lots to keep budding writers motivated!

If you would like to order further copies of this book, or any of our other titles, then please give us a call or order via your online account.

Young Writers
Remus House
Coltsfoot Drive
Peterborough
PE2 9BF
(01733) 890066
info@youngwriters.co.uk

Join in the conversation!
Tips, news, giveaways and much more!

YoungWritersUK YoungWritersCW youngwriterscw

Scan me to watch The Big Green video!